Seek & Find

Kidsbooks®

Visit us at www.kidsbooks.com

SEEK & FIND
in
Bamboo Town

- [ ] Apple
- [ ] Backpack
- [ ] Birds (3)
- [ ] Bone
- [ ] Bucket
- [ ] Cactus
- [ ] Cat
- [ ] Chair
- [ ] Crowns (2)
- [ ] Feather
- [ ] Fish (3)
- [ ] Hammer
- [ ] Hoe
- [ ] Key
- [ ] Kiddie pool
- [ ] Mailbox
- [ ] Mushroom
- [ ] Photographer
- [ ] Pie
- [ ] Pitcher
- [ ] Pitchfork
- [ ] Pumpkin
- [ ] Record
- [ ] Scissors
- [ ] Screwdriver
- [ ] Umbrella

Answers on the back.

ANSWERS

SEEK & FIND
at the
Big Fun Park

- [ ] Baby dinosaurs (2)
- [ ] Balloon
- [ ] Banana peel
- [ ] Benches (2)
- [ ] Blue jay
- [ ] Boot
- [ ] Cactus
- [ ] Cat
- [ ] Coffeepot
- [ ] Dollar sign
- [ ] Elephants (3)
- [ ] Fire hydrant
- [ ] Giraffes (2)
- [ ] Hamburgers (3)
- [ ] Kite
- [ ] Mice (2)
- [ ] Monkey
- [ ] Necklace
- [ ] Owl
- [ ] Pelican
- [ ] Penguin
- [ ] Pigs (5)
- [ ] Sailboat
- [ ] Sailor hat
- [ ] Scarecrow
- [ ] Skull

Answers on the back.

BEGINNERS

Bull · Popcorn-eating dino · Billy goat · Pencil · Bear · Chicken · Lamppost · Dinosaur clown · Flying reptile · Duck · Seal · Police worm

ANSWERS

SEEK & FIND
at the
Roller Rink

- ☐ Arrow
- ☐ Baby
- ☐ Balloons (3)
- ☐ Bird
- ☐ Boxer
- ☐ Candle
- ☐ Clowns (2)
- ☐ Deer
- ☐ Dogs (3)
- ☐ Fairy godmother
- ☐ Hamburger
- ☐ Jester's hat
- ☐ Jump rope
- ☐ Knight
- ☐ Lampshade
- ☐ Letter carrier
- ☐ Manhole
- ☐ Paintbrushes (2)
- ☐ "Pigman"
- ☐ Pillow
- ☐ Pizza
- ☐ Robot
- ☐ Sheep
- ☐ Sombrero
- ☐ Telephone
- ☐ Television

Answers on the back.

ANSWERS

SEEK & FIND
in the
Arcade

Answers on the back.

BEGINNERS

Angel
Drum
Bee
Bathtub
Target
Alligator
Flying bat
Hat
Foot
Horseshoe
Top
Wood
Umbrella

ANSWERS

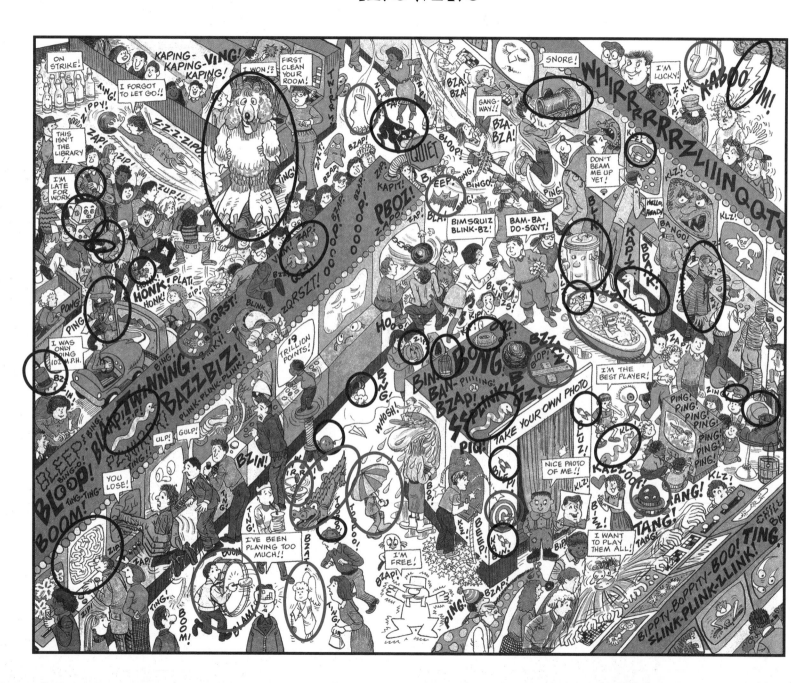

SEEK & FIND
at the
Aquarium

- [ ] Backpack
- [ ] Bottle
- [ ] Camera
- [ ] Cowboy
- [ ] Doghouses (2)
- [ ] Electric eel
- [ ] Faucet
- [ ] Ghost
- [ ] Green handbag
- [ ] Lamp
- [ ] Mermaid
- [ ] Net
- [ ] Rowboat
- [ ] Sailboat
- [ ] Sailor hat
- [ ] Scooter
- [ ] Seahorse
- [ ] Snorkel & mask
- [ ] Snowman
- [ ] Snowshoes
- [ ] Starfish (3)
- [ ] Stingray
- [ ] Swords (2)
- [ ] Teacher
- [ ] Telescope
- [ ] Tic-tac-toe

Answers on the back.

BEGINNERS

Flying fish
Igloo
Robot
Boot
Rocking horse
Fire hydrant
Guitar
Duck
Mushroom
Life preserver
Pirate
Lightbulb

ANSWERS

SEEK & FIND
at the
Zoo

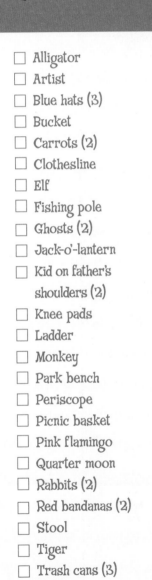

- [ ] Alligator
- [ ] Artist
- [ ] Blue hats (3)
- [ ] Bucket
- [ ] Carrots (2)
- [ ] Clothesline
- [ ] Elf
- [ ] Fishing pole
- [ ] Ghosts (2)
- [ ] Jack-o'-lantern
- [ ] Kid on father's shoulders (2)
- [ ] Knee pads
- [ ] Ladder
- [ ] Monkey
- [ ] Park bench
- [ ] Periscope
- [ ] Picnic basket
- [ ] Pink flamingo
- [ ] Quarter moon
- [ ] Rabbits (2)
- [ ] Red bandanas (2)
- [ ] Stool
- [ ] Tiger
- [ ] Trash cans (3)
- [ ] Zebras (2)

Answers on the back.

BEGINNERS

Hippo

Purple sock

Matador

Telescope

Turtle

Cowboy

Robin Hood

Lion

Jumping boy

Kite

Skateboarder

Orange bird

Tire

ANSWERS

- [ ] Benches (2)
- [ ] Bowling ball
- [ ] Candle
- [ ] Clowns (2)
- [ ] Crayon
- [ ] Dogs (2)
- [ ] Dripping faucet
- [ ] Duck
- [ ] Fish
- [ ] Flowerpots (2)
- [ ] Handbag
- [ ] Hard hat
- [ ] Jogger
- [ ] Man sleeping
- [ ] Moose
- [ ] Mouse ears
- [ ] Newspaper
- [ ] Peanut
- [ ] Postal worker
- [ ] Ostrich
- [ ] Sailor hats (2)
- [ ] Scarecrow
- [ ] Sombrero
- [ ] Suspenders (3 sets)
- [ ] Tepee
- [ ] Toothbrush

Answers on the back.

ANSWERS

SEEK & FIND
at the
Beach

BEGINNERS

Bunch of balloons · Pickle barrel · Birdbath · Policeman · Lifeguard · Clown · Detective · Surfboard · Shark · Castaway · Raft · Crocodile

- ☐ Beach ball
- ☐ Bottles with notes (3)
- ☐ Broom
- ☐ Castle
- ☐ Cow
- ☐ Cruise ship
- ☐ Diving board
- ☐ Flying disc
- ☐ Flying fish (4)
- ☐ Hearts (3)
- ☐ Horse
- ☐ Kite
- ☐ Litter bug
- ☐ Lost swim trunks
- ☐ Lunch box
- ☐ Merman
- ☐ Motorcycle
- ☐ Mummy
- ☐ Palm trees (3)
- ☐ Sailors (2)
- ☐ Sea horse
- ☐ Sea serpent
- ☐ Starfish (9)
- ☐ Submarine
- ☐ Swans (2)
- ☐ Tricycle

Answers on the back.

ANSWERS

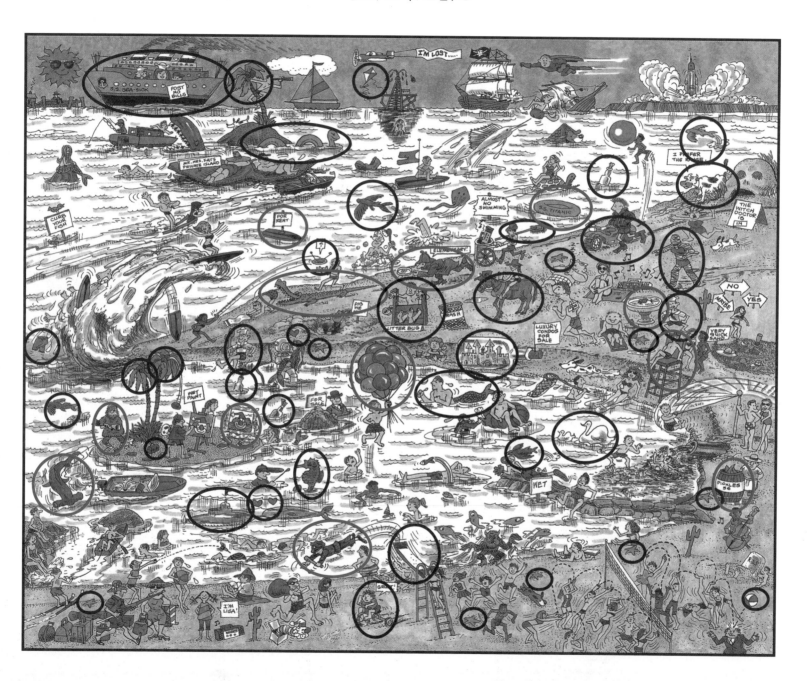

SEEK & FIND
at the
Super
Supermarket

- [ ] Bandanas (3)
- [ ] Bare foot
- [ ] Broom
- [ ] Chef
- [ ] Cobweb
- [ ] Cowboy
- [ ] Crown
- [ ] Dog fish
- [ ] Eggs
- [ ] Firefighter
- [ ] Fire hydrant
- [ ] Fishing pole
- [ ] Handbag
- [ ] Knee pads
- [ ] Paddles (2)
- [ ] Pear
- [ ] People sleeping (2)
- [ ] Pocket watch
- [ ] Pole-vaulter
- [ ] Propeller
- [ ] Roller skates
- [ ] Scarves (2)
- [ ] Snake
- [ ] Straw
- [ ] Sunglasses
- [ ] Tin Man

Answers on the back.

ANSWERS

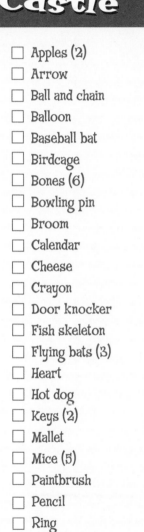

SEEK & FIND
in the
Creepy Castle

- ☐ Apples (2)
- ☐ Arrow
- ☐ Ball and chain
- ☐ Balloon
- ☐ Baseball bat
- ☐ Birdcage
- ☐ Bones (6)
- ☐ Bowling pin
- ☐ Broom
- ☐ Calendar
- ☐ Cheese
- ☐ Crayon
- ☐ Door knocker
- ☐ Fish skeleton
- ☐ Flying bats (3)
- ☐ Heart
- ☐ Hot dog
- ☐ Keys (2)
- ☐ Mallet
- ☐ Mice (5)
- ☐ Paintbrush
- ☐ Pencil
- ☐ Ring
- ☐ Skateboard
- ☐ Steak
- ☐ Zipper

Answers on the back.

ANSWERS

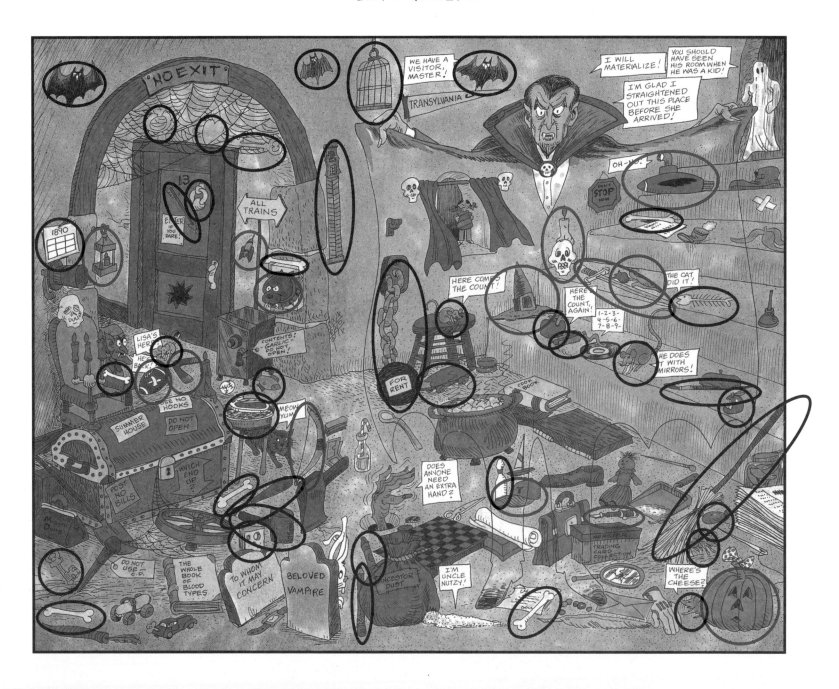

SEEK & FIND at Exciting Experiments

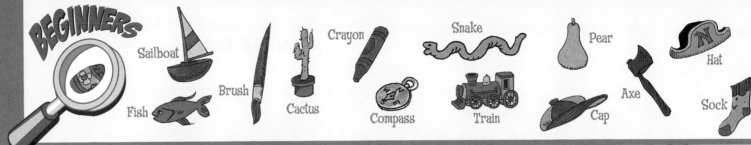

Answers on the back.

ANSWERS

BEGINNERS

Deer
Mouse
Hammer
Pot
Pig
Snail
Beach umbrella
Grapes
Turtle
Elephant
Submarine
Baseball bat
Mushroom
Pumpkin

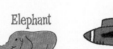

- [ ] Axe
- [ ] Barrel
- [ ] Beach ball
- [ ] Bird
- [ ] Book
- [ ] Bowl
- [ ] Brushes (2)
- [ ] Candle
- [ ] Cane
- [ ] Cat
- [ ] Dog
- [ ] Drums (2)
- [ ] Eyeglasses
- [ ] Fish
- [ ] Flying bat
- [ ] Frog
- [ ] Hair bows (5)
- [ ] Kites (2)
- [ ] Moon
- [ ] Puddles (4)
- [ ] Ring
- [ ] Slice of pizza
- [ ] Stars (3)
- [ ] Surfer
- [ ] Worm

ANSWERS

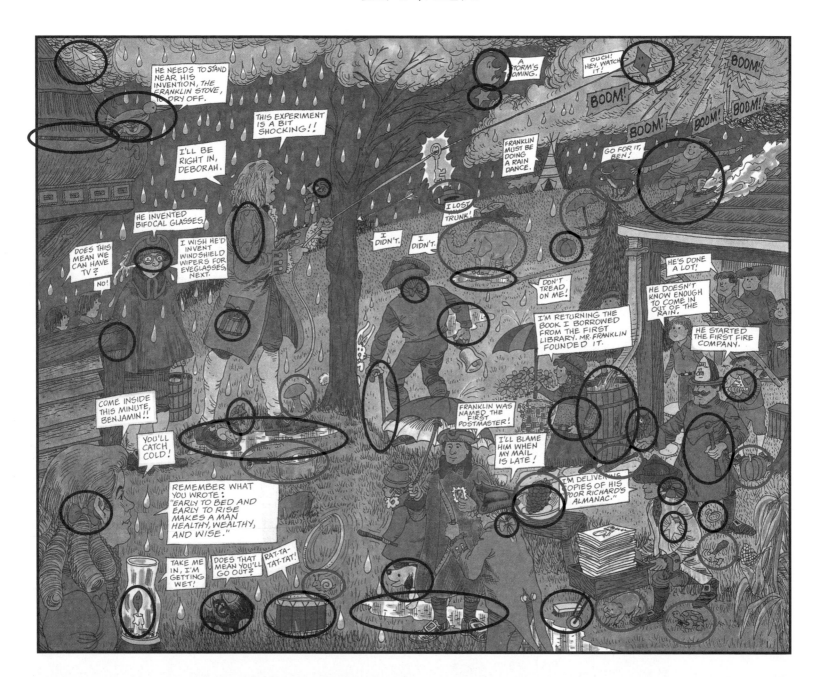

SEEK & FIND in Napoleon's France

Answers on the back.

BEGINNERS — Poodle, Cat, Hat, Key, Turtle, Watering can, Eight ball, Cake on wheels, Sweeper, Horse, Medal, Jack-o'-lantern

ANSWERS

SEEK & FIND in Monsterville

- [ ] Broken heart
- [ ] Bucket
- [ ] Cowboy hat
- [ ] Flowers (2)
- [ ] "For Rent" gravestone
- [ ] Gorilla
- [ ] Hose
- [ ] Key
- [ ] Mailbox
- [ ] Mousehole
- [ ] Ms. Transylvania
- [ ] Mummy
- [ ] Number 13 (3)
- [ ] One-eyed monster
- [ ] Owl
- [ ] Pig
- [ ] Pile of bones
- [ ] Pink hand
- [ ] Pyramid
- [ ] Rat
- [ ] Scary trees (2)
- [ ] Skeleton
- [ ] Skulls (8)
- [ ] Stethoscope
- [ ] Three-legged ghost
- [ ] Tin Man

Answers on the back.

BEGINNERS

Bird monster

Sign

Truck

Flying carpet

Tin can

Bug

Letter carrier

Parachute

Green monster

Witch

Pink snake monster

Wizard

ANSWERS

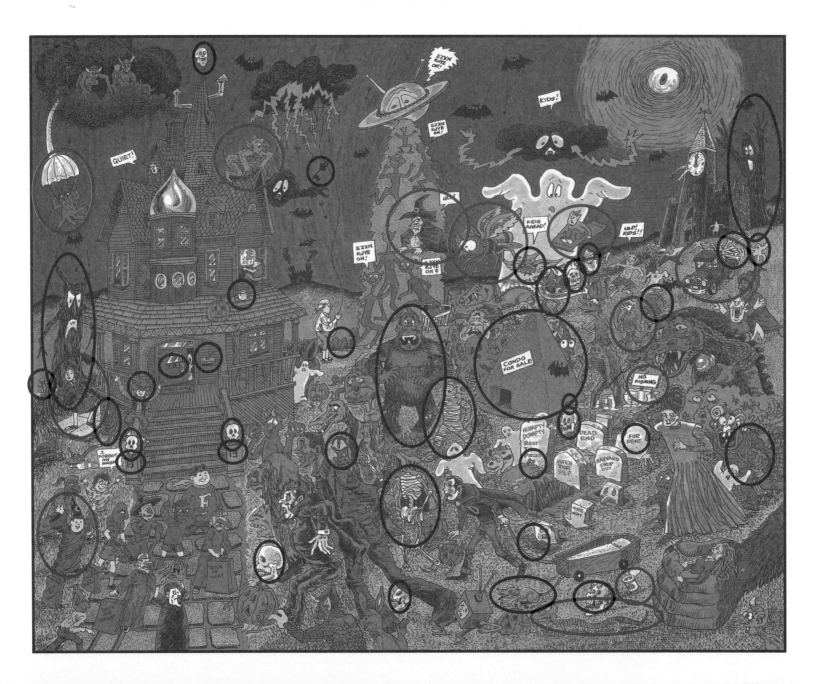

SEEK & FIND at the Museum

BEGINNERS

- Alien
- Dog with bone
- Flying carpet
- Kid reading
- Sad balloon
- Birthday cake
- "First Prize"
- Football player
- Hot-dog cart
- Airplane
- Knight
- Rowboat
- Scuba diver

- [ ] Bees (3)
- [ ] Bicyclist
- [ ] Birdcage
- [ ] Caveman
- [ ] Doghouse
- [ ] Elephant
- [ ] Firefighter
- [ ] Fire hydrant
- [ ] Fishing pole
- [ ] Hammock
- [ ] Hot-air balloon
- [ ] Ice-cream cone
- [ ] Jack-in-the-box
- [ ] Juggler
- [ ] Kite
- [ ] Long beard
- [ ] Magnifying glasses (2)
- [ ] Pizza delivery
- [ ] Pyramid
- [ ] Quicksand
- [ ] Robin Hood
- [ ] Rope climber
- [ ] Sailing ships (2)
- [ ] Superman
- [ ] Telescopes (2)
- [ ] Tic-tac-toe

Answers on the back.

ANSWERS

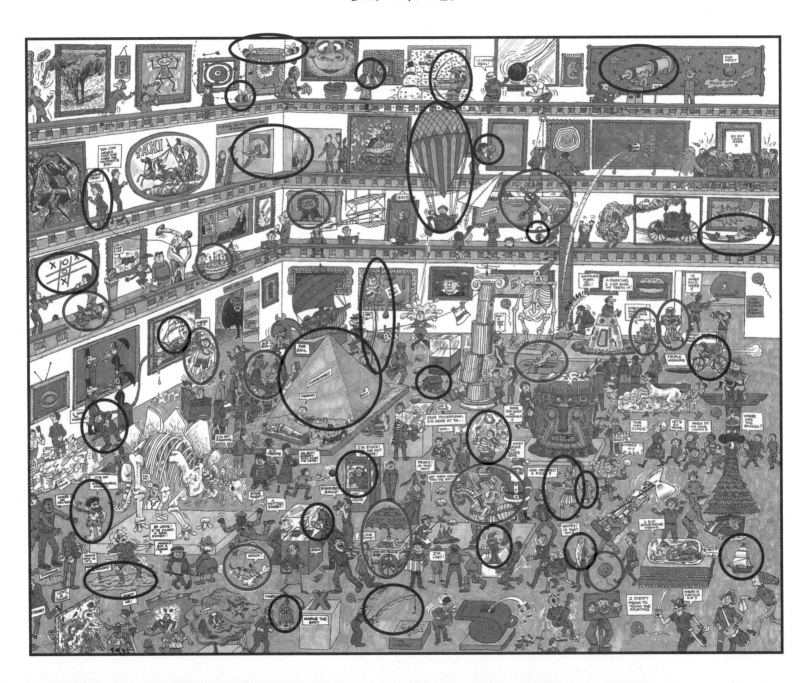

SEEK & FIND
in
Prehistoric Times

- [ ] Candle
- [ ] Cherry
- [ ] Clothespin
- [ ] Dinosaur egg
- [ ] Faucet
- [ ] Four-leaf clover
- [ ] Hammer
- [ ] Hot chocolate
- [ ] Life preserver
- [ ] Message in a bottle
- [ ] Necklace
- [ ] Necktie
- [ ] "No U Turn" sign
- [ ] Palm trees (3)
- [ ] Periscope
- [ ] Pizza
- [ ] Skateboard
- [ ] Spool of thread
- [ ] Stars (2)
- [ ] Swimming duck
- [ ] Tire
- [ ] Top hat
- [ ] Umbrella
- [ ] Volcanoes (2)
- [ ] Wooden wheel

BEGINNERS

Green-and-yellow dinosaur

Baby carriage

Book

Bird

Ice-cream cone

Rat

Piggy bank

Hockey stick

Ring

Flying reptile

Sock

Scarecrow

Coffeepot

Tent

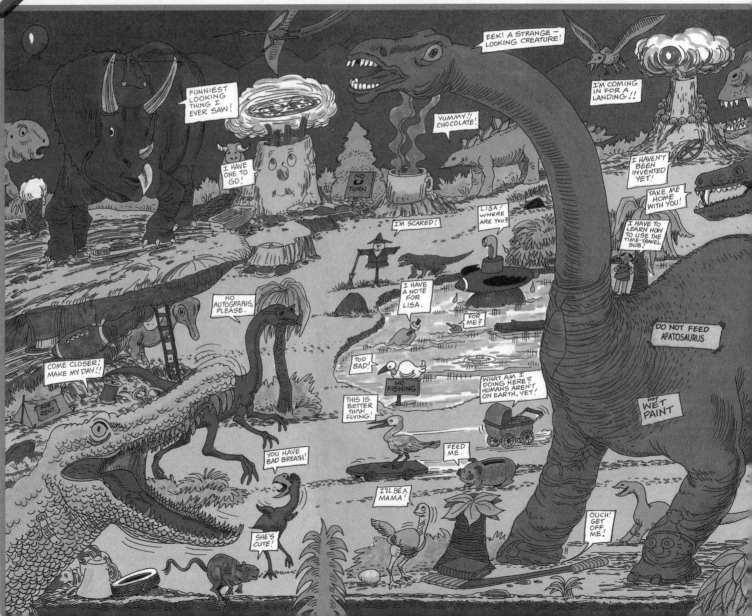

ANSWERS

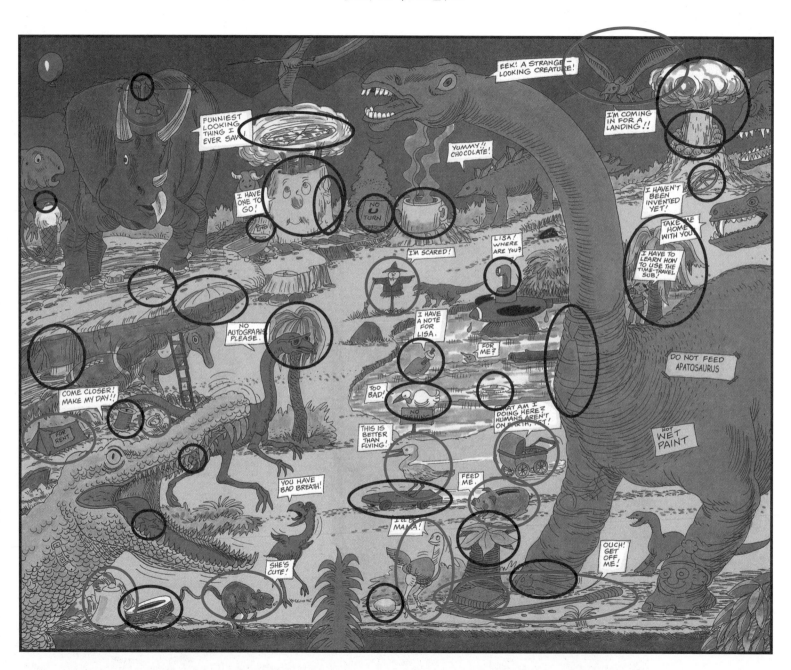

SEEK & FIND
at the
Rock-and-Roll
Show

- [ ] Accordion
- [ ] Bandana
- [ ] Banjo
- [ ] Baton
- [ ] Bow tie
- [ ] Broken nose
- [ ] Bubblegum bubble
- [ ] Cameras (5)
- [ ] Elephant
- [ ] Feather
- [ ] Fiddle
- [ ] Flags (2)
- [ ] Flying bat
- [ ] Football helmet
- [ ] Giraffe
- [ ] Harmonica
- [ ] Hearts (2)
- [ ] King Kong
- [ ] Microphones (2)
- [ ] Paper airplane
- [ ] Propeller hat
- [ ] Scarf
- [ ] Speaker
- [ ] Stage lights (6)
- [ ] Turtle
- [ ] Witch

Answers on the back.

BEGINNERS

Submarine

Pumpkin

Girl

Straw hat

Trombone

Rabbit

Mailbox

Balloon

Red wagon

Green hat

Purple hat

Red Hat

ANSWERS

BEGINNERS

 Candle

 Clamp

 Turtle

 Poodle

 Lightbulb

 Umbrella

 Phonograph

 Birdcage · Cat · Dog

 Safe

 Typewriter

- [ ] Briefcase
- [ ] Chairs (2)
- [ ] Clipboards (2)
- [ ] Club
- [ ] Cookies
- [ ] Cowboy hats (4)
- [ ] Curtains
- [ ] Duck
- [ ] Eyeglasses
- [ ] Feather
- [ ] Film projector
- [ ] Hammer
- [ ] Pail
- [ ] Pencils (2)
- [ ] Periscope
- [ ] Picture
- [ ] Pillow
- [ ] Plant
- [ ] Rain slicker
- [ ] Roller skates
- [ ] Sailing ship
- [ ] Screw
- [ ] Shadow
- [ ] Sheep
- [ ] Stool
- [ ] Triangle

Answers on the back.

ANSWERS

SEEK & FIND
in Cat City

 BEGINNERS

 Bus-stop sign
 Police officer
 Ice-skater
 Mouse
 Skateboarder
 Sled
 Traffic light

Boat on wheels
Catmobile
Rocket
Clock
Roller skater
Train
Trash can

- [ ] Airplane
- [ ] Antenna
- [ ] Balloons (2)
- [ ] Barrel
- [ ] Blimp
- [ ] Candle
- [ ] Cracked window
- [ ] Fire hydrant
- [ ] Flat tire
- [ ] Fur coat
- [ ] Hammer
- [ ] Hard hats (3)
- [ ] Mailbox
- [ ] Manhole cover
- [ ] Motorcycle
- [ ] Octopus
- [ ] Penguin
- [ ] Piano
- [ ] Red bow
- [ ] Rooster
- [ ] Shovel
- [ ] Sun
- [ ] Telephone booth
- [ ] Toolbox
- [ ] Towel
- [ ] Turtle

Answers on the back.

ANSWERS

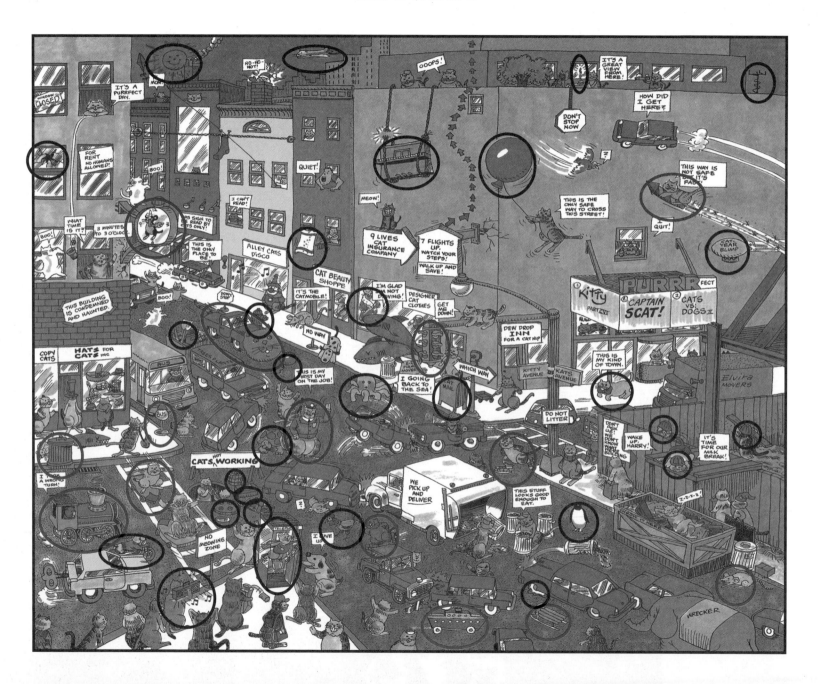

SEEK & FIND at the Mad Mall

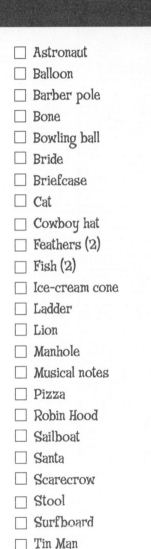

- [ ] Astronaut
- [ ] Balloon
- [ ] Barber pole
- [ ] Bone
- [ ] Bowling ball
- [ ] Bride
- [ ] Briefcase
- [ ] Cat
- [ ] Cowboy hat
- [ ] Feathers (2)
- [ ] Fish (2)
- [ ] Ice-cream cone
- [ ] Ladder
- [ ] Lion
- [ ] Manhole
- [ ] Musical notes
- [ ] Pizza
- [ ] Robin Hood
- [ ] Sailboat
- [ ] Santa
- [ ] Scarecrow
- [ ] Stool
- [ ] Surfboard
- [ ] Tin Man
- [ ] Tuba
- [ ] Turtle

Answers on the back.

BEGINNERS

Shopping bag · Drum · Dog · Umbrella · Birdhouse · Jack-o'-lantern · Skier · King · Moon · Rabbit · Parachute · Mouse

ANSWERS

ANSWERS

SEEK & FIND
at the
Spooky Mansion

- [ ] Arrows (2)
- [ ] Button
- [ ] Candle
- [ ] Carrot
- [ ] Cauldron
- [ ] Cupcake
- [ ] Curtains
- [ ] Flowerpot
- [ ] Football
- [ ] Ghost
- [ ] Kite
- [ ] Lawn mower
- [ ] Letter
- [ ] Medal
- [ ] Ring
- [ ] Shovel
- [ ] Skulls (2)
- [ ] Sled
- [ ] Spiderweb
- [ ] Sword
- [ ] Swordfish
- [ ] Tin can
- [ ] Trash can lid
- [ ] Vulture
- [ ] Watering can

Answers on the back.

BEGINNERS

Book

Flashlight

Brush

Mug

Pot

Tire

Piano keys

Flying bat

Bucket

Wagon

Pencil

Jack-o'-lantern

Skateboard

Umbrella

ANSWERS

SEEK & FIND at the Disco

BEGINNERS

Duck

Cat wearing a bow tie

Snow cat

Police officer

Rollerskating cat

Rabbit

Cat blowing horn

Cat in a blue suit

Cat in a red suit

Skier

Sultan

- ☐ Ballerina
- ☐ Blue rhinos (2)
- ☐ Break-dancer
- ☐ Chef
- ☐ Clown
- ☐ Cowboy
- ☐ Disco ball
- ☐ Dog
- ☐ Earplug seller
- ☐ Earrings (2)
- ☐ Eye patch
- ☐ Flowerpot
- ☐ Hardhat
- ☐ Headband
- ☐ Karate cat
- ☐ Lampshade
- ☐ Mice (2)
- ☐ Pig
- ☐ Pirate's sword
- ☐ Pizza
- ☐ Record player
- ☐ Sleeping cat
- ☐ Speakers (10)
- ☐ Sunglasses
- ☐ Swinging cat
- ☐ Top hat

Answers on the back.

ANSWERS

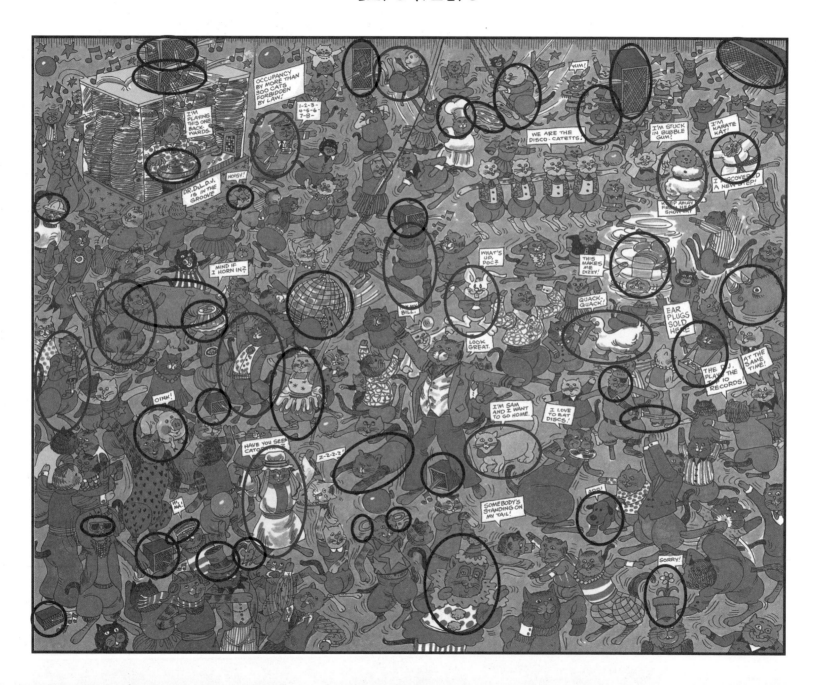

SEEK & FIND in Fast Food Heaven

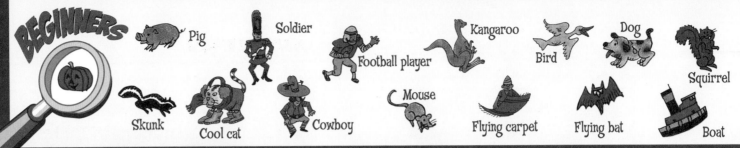

BEGINNERS

- Pig
- Soldier
- Football player
- Kangaroo
- Bird
- Dog
- Squirrel
- Skunk
- Cool cat
- Cowboy
- Mouse
- Flying carpet
- Flying bat
- Boat

- [ ] Alligator
- [ ] Bone
- [ ] Bowling ball
- [ ] Carrot
- [ ] Club
- [ ] Crowns (2)
- [ ] Drum
- [ ] Elf
- [ ] Frog
- [ ] Ghosts (2)
- [ ] Ice-cream cone
- [ ] Igloo
- [ ] Jack-o'-lantern
- [ ] Jogger
- [ ] Kite
- [ ] Octopus
- [ ] Owl
- [ ] Pickle
- [ ] Popped balloon
- [ ] Rabbit
- [ ] Shopping bag
- [ ] Skier
- [ ] Snowman
- [ ] Tire
- [ ] Trees (2)
- [ ] UFO

Answers on the back.

ANSWERS

SEEK & FIND
at the
Basketball Game

- [ ] Alligator
- [ ] Balloons (2)
- [ ] Baseball
- [ ] Cannon
- [ ] Clown
- [ ] Elephant
- [ ] Envelopes (2)
- [ ] Eyeglasses (2)
- [ ] Football helmet
- [ ] Frog
- [ ] Headbands (2)
- [ ] Hot dog
- [ ] Ice skate
- [ ] Kangaroo
- [ ] Lost glove
- [ ] Necktie
- [ ] "No Parking"
- [ ] Police officer
- [ ] Pom poms (4)
- [ ] Rabbit
- [ ] Saw
- [ ] Slice of pizza
- [ ] Snake
- [ ] Stars (3)
- [ ] Tarzan
- [ ] TV camera

Answers on the back.

BEGINNERS

Bird · Baseball bat · Dog · Jack-o'-lantern · Bowling ball · Fish · Ghost · Pencil · Kite · Mouse · Whistle · Bucket · Turtle

ANSWERS

SEEK & FIND
on the
Water Ride

BEGINNERS

Duck surfing
Wind-up dinosaur
Popsicle
Mouse
Turtle
Fire hydrant

Bird
Hot dog
Goose
Paint bucket
Parrot
Yellow dinosaur
Sci-fi star

- [ ] Apple
- [ ] Beach ball
- [ ] Bib
- [ ] Candles (2)
- [ ] Cats (2)
- [ ] Crutches (2)
- [ ] Cupcake
- [ ] Earring
- [ ] Elephants (2)
- [ ] Fishing pole
- [ ] Gorilla
- [ ] Hearts (3)
- [ ] Kangaroo
- [ ] Paper bag
- [ ] Periscope
- [ ] Peter Pan
- [ ] Picnic basket
- [ ] Pitcher
- [ ] Puddles (4)
- [ ] Rabbits (2)
- [ ] Scuba diver
- [ ] Sea horse
- [ ] Sheep
- [ ] Snakes (2)
- [ ] Sunglasses (2)
- [ ] Tents (3)

Answers on the back.

ANSWERS

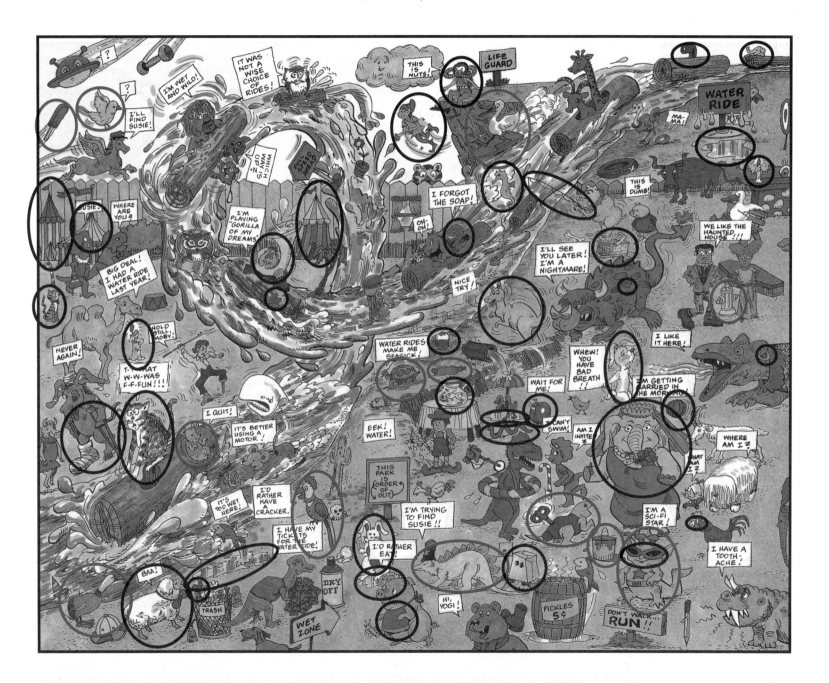

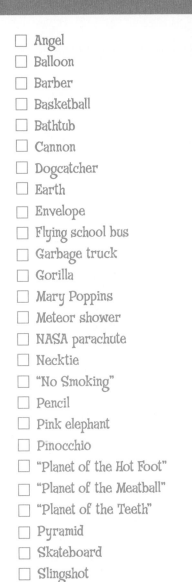

SEEK & FIND in Space

Answers on the back.

BEGINNERS

Barbell
Doghouse
Flying horse
Rocking chair
Seal
Polka-dot shorts
Alien
Cow
Fish
Airplane
Scissors
Red spray paint
Traffic light

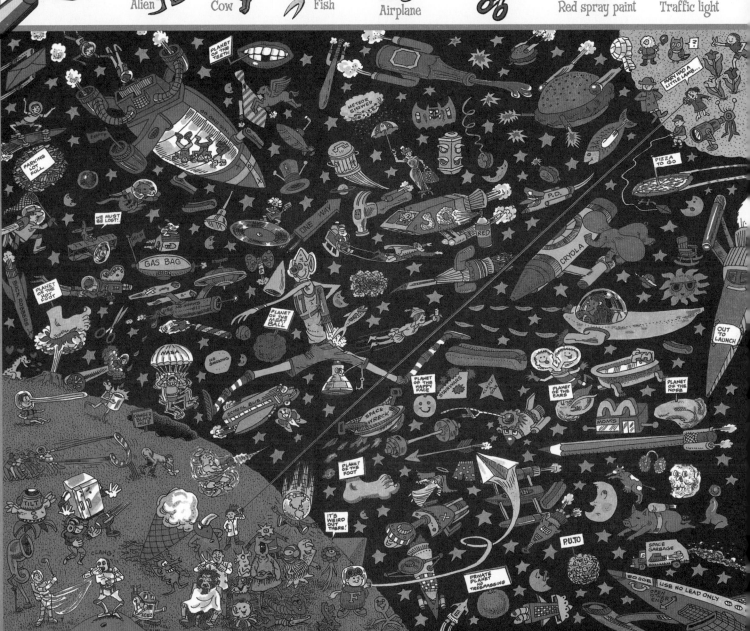

ANSWERS

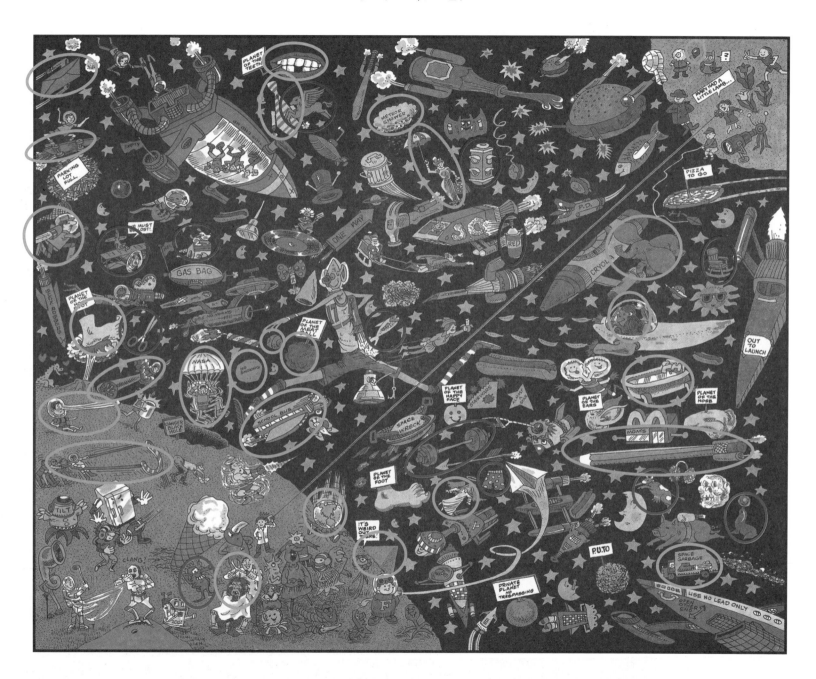

SEEK & FIND at the Cats' Serenade

BEGINNERS

Dog dish (HECTOR) · Piggy bank · Witch · Can · Pillow · Yo-yo · Boot · Singing star · Cannon · Mouse · Doll · Jack-o'-lantern · Stool

- ☐ Baseball
- ☐ Baseball bat
- ☐ Birds (2)
- ☐ Bones (2)
- ☐ Cloud
- ☐ Fishbowl
- ☐ Fish skeletons (2)
- ☐ Flowerpots (3)
- ☐ Football
- ☐ Ghost
- ☐ Light
- ☐ Microphone
- ☐ Moon
- ☐ "No Cats Welcome" mat
- ☐ Old tire
- ☐ Police car
- ☐ Policeman
- ☐ Pot
- ☐ Record player
- ☐ Rhino
- ☐ Rolling pin
- ☐ Spoon
- ☐ Stacks of paper (2)
- ☐ Stars (4)
- ☐ Table
- ☐ Tepee

Answers on the back.

ANSWERS

SEEK & FIND
at
Detective Donald's

BEGINNERS

Flyswatter
Bird
Hourglass
Medal
Shovel
Saw
Pencil
Boot
Cheese
Hamburger
Key
Owl
Football
Magazine

- ☐ Apple core
- ☐ Broken pencils (3)
- ☐ Calendar
- ☐ Candles (3)
- ☐ Chalk
- ☐ Chalkboard
- ☐ Comb
- ☐ Cupcake
- ☐ Diploma
- ☐ Fan
- ☐ Feather
- ☐ Fishing pole
- ☐ Hockey stick
- ☐ Jacket
- ☐ Ladder
- ☐ Lamp
- ☐ "Milk crate"
- ☐ Mirror
- ☐ Pail of water
- ☐ Pizza
- ☐ Skull
- ☐ Snake
- ☐ Stack of envelopes
- ☐ Sword
- ☐ Tin can
- ☐ Upside-down tack

Answers on the back.

ANSWERS

SEEK & FIND
in
Ancient Egypt

Answers on the back.

ANSWERS

SEEK & FIND with Friendly Aliens

BEGINNERS

Cactus · Sled · Guitar · Apple · Spoon · Top hat · Trash can · Book · Cap · Crayon · Door · Train · Pie Man · Airplane · Sea horse

- [ ] Basketball hoop
- [ ] Briefcase
- [ ] Clothespin
- [ ] Comb
- [ ] Cup
- [ ] Curtain
- [ ] Desk lamp
- [ ] Donut
- [ ] Envelope
- [ ] Fire hydrants (2)
- [ ] Flower
- [ ] Football
- [ ] Hamburger
- [ ] Hose
- [ ] Musical notes
- [ ] "No Parking" sign
- [ ] Paintbrush
- [ ] Pencils (2)
- [ ] Pirates (2)
- [ ] Pyramid
- [ ] Straw
- [ ] Target
- [ ] Television
- [ ] Tepee
- [ ] Trees (3)
- [ ] Yo-yo

Answers on the back.

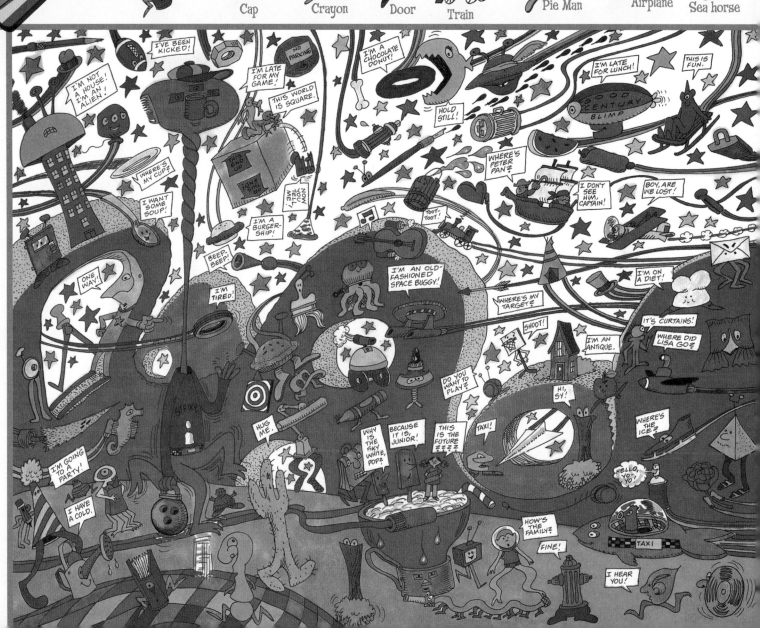